Dear Elizabeth

by
GENE MACKEY and HELEN SWAN

KIDSRIGHTS

The authors are grateful to Roland Summit,
M.D., and to the young women attending
the Child Sexual Abuse Treatment Programs
of Johnson County and Wyandotte County,
Kansas, for reviewing this book.

DEAR ELIZABETH
Copyright © 1993, 1991, 1989,
Helen Swan and Gene Mackey, text
Copyright © 1993, 1991, KIDSRIGHTS,
illustrations

Published by:
KIDSRIGHTS ®
        10100 Park Cedar Drive
        Charlotte, NC 28210
        800/892-KIDS   704/541-0100
        FAX 704/541-0113

10 9 8 7 6 5 4

Fourth printing.

Printed in the United States of
America

ISBN: 1-55864-007-X

INTRODUCTION

DEAR ELIZABETH is a compilation of three diaries kept by a fifteen-year-old girl named Brenda who has been sexually abused by her father. Brenda is a fictional character, but the experiences and feelings she shares in her diary are absolutely real for millions of people.

This is a book dedicated to helping and informing these people--as well as the relatives, friends, psychologists, psychiatrists and social workers who are concerned about them and about the general problem of sexual abuse in today's society.

TO THERAPISTS

Those who provide counseling for sexually abused young people--whether individually or in group--may use this book as a catalyst to the process of opening up painful memories and feelings.

Brenda's story supports the idea that sharing frightening secrets can start a person on the road to survival and triumph and away from abuse and fear. Her story acknowledges that adolescents commonly drop out of therapy too soon and encourages the resumption of therapy.

The course of Brenda's confrontation with sexual abuse in her life offers a role model of hope for similarly troubled young people. Quite a lot of factual detailed discussion of specific therapeutic issues can be found in the Afterword.

TO YOUNG PEOPLE WHO HAVE BEEN SEXUALLY ABUSED

This book is a sharing of feelings and thoughts about sexual abuse. It is a story about pain, hope and survival. It is also a story about a fifteen-year-old girl who has all the everyday dreams and worries of adolescents who have not been abused. It is a story about school, home, parents, boyfriends, daydreams and laughter--things we all share just because we are human beings. It is not a book that has to be studied like a textbook; it can be read simply as a story.

Find a good, quiet place to read if you can, a place where you won't be distracted too much, a place where you are comfortable. Then sit back and let the story happen in your mind as you read. Stop anytime you want to and think about the story--or just take a rest from it. You may want to read it all in one sitting (it is a short book) or you may want to read just a little bit at a time--it is entirely up to you.

If you have questions or concerns ask the person who gave you this book or someone you trust. There are many answers, much information and numerous people who are willing to help. You have a right to get the information and help you need--just as Brenda does in the story you are about to read.

First
Diary

🐢 11:30 pm, Sept 7 My room 🐢

Dear...you.

Who are you?

A diary? Dear Diary...

I always thought that would be a dumb way to start one...Dear Diary...How are you Diary?

No answer.

The paper just lies here in the notebook on my lap--blank, except where I've written, and silent. Blank and silent--like me.

And you.

I don't know who you are. I don't know why I'm writing this to you. I don't know if you will ever read it. I doubt it.

I'm using a loose leaf notebook; so if anyone sees me writing this they'll think I'm just doing homework. And I can easily take out the pages I've written. No one could tell they were gone.

After I took them out I could tear them up. I've done it before. First, in half, then in quarters, then eighths. And keep on until the pieces are so small no one can ever read one word or paste it all together and read the sentences. But just to make sure, hold the pieces under the faucet till they are soaked and the ink runs. Then flush them down the toilet. And even if a sewer worker accidentally finds them down there somewhere he won't have any luck reading it because the pieces are too small and the ink is blurred. I could do that. I have before.

Or I could burn the pages in Daddy's ashtray and then dump the ashes in the wastebasket under some other trash; so no one would notice and ask what was burned. (Although I have an answer for that too: a paper plate caught on fire by the stove.) And then I would spray air freshener so no one could smell the burned smell. I could do that. I have before.

Or I could fold the pages very tightly, running my thumbnail along each crease to be sure it would stay folded. And then I could stand on my vanity chair and reach the top of my chest of drawers where my doll, Elizabeth, sits on an old doily, watching and not blinking. I could lift her head--the bands inside are stretched; so it is easy to lift her head up from her neck. And then I could slip my folded papers into the opening and drop them down inside Elizabeth. The pages would be safe and hidden down there. Safe and hidden in the darkness there. Never moving. Because Elizabeth never moves from that spot on the doily way up high on my chest of drawers where she sits and watches, never blinking, never telling.

Elizabeth.

She keeps my secrets. She always has, ever since Great Grandma (Mom's grandmother!) gave her to me when I was six--right before she died in the old gray house by the lake. Great Grandmother disappeared, but Elizabeth stayed. She has never left my room since I was six. I'm fourteen now and too old to play with dolls, but I keep Elizabeth up there as decoration. She's pretty and makes my room look better. And she has seen everything that has happened to me in this room. Everything. She keeps my secrets.

When I was seven, and it first happened, Elizabeth was there, her eyes wide open staring at the wall. And I was lying here on my bed, my eyes wide open, staring at Elizabeth. And Daddy talked and talked in a real low mumble--he couldn't seem to move his lips, as if they were frozen or numb. And the cigarette he smoked was shaky as a hummingbird in his hand till he put it out in the ashtray in his other hand and set it down on the floor so he could put both his hands on me, on my legs, on my vagina (a word I didn't know then, but I know now). When he put his fingers there it made me want to pee, and I said "I've gotta go to the bathroom." And he let me up to go, mumbling something I couldn't understand at all.

I went into the bathroom and peed. I looked at where he touched me. I stayed in there a long time, afraid to go back to my bedroom. I heard him breathing in there, sucking on another cigarette, blowing out the smoke, shifting his weight on my bed. I heard the click of his lighter five times--five cigarettes slowly smoked through--before I finally heard him get up and leave my room. Still I waited a long time before I came out. When I did there was still smoke in the air from all those cigarettes. Stale smoke. And his smell.

For a long time I sat on my bed and stared at Elizabeth, and she stared at the wall. Only she wasn't really staring. She was only porcelain and paint and glass eyes and fake hair, and her eyes saw nothing really. She heard nothing, smelled nothing, tasted nothing. Her skin didn't feel hands touching her, and she didn't even have a vagina.

I have stared at her a lot since that first time, and I have wished I was Elizabeth instead of me. Sometimes when he is with me I look at Elizabeth and imagine that's me up there on the chest of drawers, up high and safe; and then I can't feel what he is doing to me. I am not there with him at all. I am not a part of this horrible scene on the bed. I am porcelain and paint and glass eyes and fake hair. I stare at the wall and see nothing, hear nothing, smell nothing, taste nothing. I have no feelings and no vagina. And I sit on a doily high up on top of a chest of drawers, undisturbed and safe. I am a doll.

That's what he calls me--little doll baby. That's what I am. Move my arms, my legs, turn my head, comb my hair, change my dress. Put a bow in my hair. Touch between my legs. I'm a doll baby.

Mom said she had a doll like Elizabeth but not as fancy. One time she dropped it on a street some men were fixing and hot tar stuck all over the doll's clothes and face. The tar wouldn't come off, her mother told her. And her father said to throw it away. So she did. It was ugly and sticky with all that tar, and so she threw it away, she told me. It was the best thing, she said, but she was crying when she told me.

That's one thing about a doll. You can throw it away. It's just porcelain and paint and fake hair and if it gets covered with tar and isn't pretty anymore you can just throw it away. You can fold up all the secrets in little tightly creased notes and bury them inside her. Inside me. And you can take that doll and bury it somewhere where no one will find it--not even men digging trenches for water pipes. They might dig her up and put their hands inside her to find these secret notes, but I won't let them. I will bury her deep so they won't find her.

Then you won't ever know me. Whoever you are.

No one will.

Except Elizabeth.

She knows. She understands. Or she doesn't know. She doesn't understand. Because she doesn't care, feel, think or hurt. She's a doll. And I'm a doll.

Doll baby.

Dear Elizabeth...this is for you. And me. I will tell everything, fold the secrets inside and inside me and throw you away. You can do that with dolls. Throw you away.

And me too.

5 am, Sept 8   My room

Something is about to happen. I know it is. The same feeling I had when Great Grandmother died. No one told me. I just knew. Now I know again. But it's not Great Grandmother. It's me.

12 Noon, Sept 8   School

Dear Elizabeth... I'm sitting in the lunchroom at school, but in my mind I am sitting on my bed looking up at your peaceful face. It helps me to imagine your face when I write this. Your face is so clear, so pretty, so still. It never changes. I can tell you. You won't react.

This morning at breakfast Mom told us she was off work for three nights. (She works nights at the Country Inn Restaurant, but she's not a waitress, she's a manager.) Daddy wanted to know why, and Mom said, "Oh, just because I need some rest. Warren said it would be all right."

"Well, it might be all right with Warren," Daddy said,

"but it might not be all right with me. Did you think of that?"

And Mom just kind of laughed and said, "It'll be all right. I can make it up on the weekend. Besides, it might be nice to be around here for a change." Mom looked right at me when she said that and smiled. She was trying really hard to be cheerful. But I could tell she was nervous and not really cheerful at all, just trying.

Daddy didn't want her to be cheerful, and he kept asking her questions, trying to make her mad or change her mood any way he could. But Mom just kept smiling at me and answering brightly until he gave up and just put his head down to eat his eggs covered with ketchup.

Then Matthew, my little brother, asked Mom if he could still go to Tim's house after supper. "Dad lets me go anytime I want," Matthew added, and Mom nodded again. That was true. He always got to go. But when I asked to go out Daddy always said no. Too dangerous for a girl to go out by herself, he said. Boys roaming the streets looking for trouble, he said. But my trouble was at home, not in the streets.

That doesn't matter tonight, though, because we'll all be there. All four of us. I like that when we're all home. Just like a family, any other family on the block.

❧ 12 Midnight, Sept 8 My room ❧

Tonight was not as good as I thought it would be. Mom stayed home, but Daddy kept calling her "career woman" in a sarcastic voice, and Mom wouldn't argue back. She just kept pretending she hadn't heard it and smiling and talking to me and Matthew until suddenly she just stopped. Her smiling just kind of stiffened up and strained and quivered till it wasn't smiling at all. It was crying. She put her face down in her hands on her knees as if to keep us from seeing her cry. But we saw anyway. She was sitting alone in the middle of the sofa with her flowered dress on, and the sofa had flowers too, and there was a plastic flower in the vase on the coffee table, and she just kept crying--but very softly.

Daddy didn't say a word. He just sat in his big chair looking down. Matthew got up and went to his room and closed the door. I stood up and went over to Mom, maybe to comfort her. But by then she was recovering, wiping her eyes, getting her breath. "Mom," I heard myself say, "Could I go for a walk around the block? I'll be back in ten minutes."

"Yes, Brenda," she said, "I think that would be all right." Daddy looked up and said, "It's almost dark, Martha. You want her walking the streets in the dark?"

"She'll be back before it's dark. Won't you, Brenda?"

"Yes, Mom," I said. "I just want to go around the block." Daddy smiled crooked at me and said, "Meeting that Turner boy?" I couldn't say anything. I just blushed and stared at his shoes, his big heavy shoes that were always shined.

"What if she does?" Mom said. "Scott Turner is a nice boy. Go on, Honey. It's all right."

Before anything else could happen, I turned and ran out the front door. I could hear them arguing behind me as I left. I could still hear their muffled voices as I hurried down the sidewalk past the Murrays' house to the corner. When I turned the corner and headed up Adams Street the sound of Daddy's yelling began to fade. Finally at the corner of Adams and Third

Street I couldn't hear him at all even though it was a cool, calm night, and there were hardly any other sounds.

It was nice to be outside, to breathe fresh air and hear the quietness of the street. Autumn is my favorite time of the year for several reasons. School starts in Autumn and I love school when it first starts. Everyone is kind of new and uncertain, and we are all fresh and ready for the new year. It's a starting time, a time of new teachers, new classes, new hopes.

And I like the weather in Autumn. I like the way people leave their doors and windows open instead of shutting everything up with an air conditioner whirring. I like the way families stay at home more in the Autumn. In the summer they are always coming and going, vacationing or swimming or going to the lake. In the Autumn--at least for a while it seems-- people stay home, getting organized, I guess, for the next season. I can see them in their homes at night settling in about this time of day when darkness is settling in too.

Sometimes they are watching TV or eating dinner late. Sometimes the kids are at the dining room table and the mother and father are watching TV or reading newspapers or magazines. Sometimes they are having drinks and talking. I see them and sometimes I can hear little bits of what they are saying. It's nothing really, just casual conversation about things that happened that day, plans for tomorrow. I love to watch families at home at this time and listen.

Please don't get me wrong. I'm not a Peeping Tom or anything. I just watch as I slowly walk along the sidewalk. I'm just casually observing, not spying. But I see a lot. I see what a family is, what it can be. I see how they can love and help each other and care and listen and not hurt. I see them living their lives in a well-oiled, smooth-running family machine.

In our family machine something is broken. The gears grind and make noise. The parts fly apart and collide and clatter around. Nothing works right in our family machine. It stops or moves in awful jerks with frightening noises. Screeches. And screams. And threats.

🐦 5 am, Sept 9   My room 🐦

No one is up yet except you and me, Elizabeth. The house is quiet. Matthew is asleep in his room, Mom and Dad in their room. There is no screaming. No crying. It's like another house, like one of those houses down the block.

But the clock in the living room is ticking, and time is passing, and pretty soon I'll hear Matthew's alarm go off. Then I'll hear him get up and do his exercises. That's when I go in to the kitchen to make us all breakfast.

Daddy will be there grinding coffee beans or cleaning the percolator. There's a special way of making coffee he learned in Panama when he was stationed there. He won't drink any other kind of coffee. Once Mom decided she would start making our breakfasts and she brought a jar of instant coffee. When he saw it on the counter that morning he picked it up and threw it out in the back yard. She had to go outside in her robe and get it and carry it to the trash. She said she didn't want the neighbors to see it. So now Daddy always makes his special coffee, and I always make breakfast. Mom usually sleeps late because she works at night.

Now my clock says 5:30. The clock in the living room is still ticking, but I can't see it. I wish it didn't tick. My clock by my bed is electric and doesn't make any noise. You can turn its face away and pretend time has stopped. But that ticking clock in the living room always reminds you time hasn't stopped. It's still ticking loud and nothing can stop it.

Something will happen.

I don't know what it is. Something. The clock ticks and the time is coming. Coming closer.

🐦 12 Noon, Sept 9 School 🐦

Dear Elizabeth...I'm trying to imagine I'm in my room looking at you and no one is home except us. I'm trying to imagine how quiet and peaceful it would be, because it is really noisy in the lunchroom today. Everybody is getting to know everyone again, and they are talking more and laughing louder and getting wilder. I like it better the first few days when everyone is more careful and more polite. I'm afraid to join in one of those groups that know each other so well. I'm afraid of what they might figure out about me. So I usually eat by myself. But today something really weird happened. Scott Turner came over and asked if he could join me.

I said, "Sure, go ahead." And he said, "Does that mean sit down or go ahead to some other table?" I said "I mean go ahead and sit down." And he laughed, and I laughed, and he sat down.

We talked about our classes. He was very friendly and nice and relaxed. I wasn't relaxed at all, but I don't think he knew that. When he asked why I wasn't eating anything I said I was dieting. He laughed at that and said I was skinny as a model. I didn't know what to answer. I had lied, and he caught me. I wasn't dieting. It's true I'm skinny, but not like a model, more like a scarecrow. "Oh well," I said and popped a big piece of bread in my mouth; but I couldn't chew it or swallow it. He kept on talking, saying I looked like an Italian model whose picture was on the cover of his mother's magazine. I just nodded and smiled with my mouth closed, because I didn't want him to see inside my mouth. I didn't want him to see the piece of bread. I didn't want him to know I wasn't eating. So I smiled and nodded and didn't say a word. Then I did something really stupid. I put another piece of bread in, still pretending I was eating and having a great time. Now I had two pieces of bread I couldn't chew or swallow. He kept right on talking. He didn't seem to mind that I wasn't saying anything.

After a while I started to get sick at my stomach. I was afraid I might throw up; so I took my napkin and pretended to wipe my mouth and spit the bread into the napkin. I wadded the napkin and bread up and put it under my tray edge. I think he may have known what I was doing, but he didn't let on. At least, I didn't throw up.

Finally Scott stood up and picked up his tray. "You want me to carry your tray back?" he said.

"No," I said and grabbed hold of my tray. Of course, I didn't want him to see the wadded-up napkin and bread. Then he sat back down and leaned close to me. I could smell what kind of shampoo he used.

"See you in English," he said. I just nodded. "You know, Brenda, you'd be very interesting to know more about," he said, "but I don't know anything about you at all."

"Not much to know," I said and laughed. He didn't laugh. He just said, "I bet that's not true." Then he smiled, got up and walked away.

I don't look like a model. I know I don't. I try to do my hair and make-up like the models in Glamour

Magazine, but I don't have their bone structure. My bone structure is all crooked and ugly. At least I can be neat.

I have to go to social studies now.

⁂ 11:30 pm, Sept 9   My room ⁂

All this trouble at home, all this yelling, arguing--it's my fault. Mom thinks I want her to stay home and be with me. And I do. But it's selfish. When she goes to work, and I take care of Daddy, things are smoother. He says I like it. He says I enjoy taking care of him. And that's why I can't tell. I'm just as wrong as he is.

Am I wrong? If you were here--really here--how would you answer? Wrong? As wrong as he is? Almost as wrong? All wrong? If you were my friend maybe you wouldn't think I'm as wrong as he is. But you probably wouldn't want to be friends with someone like me.

Maybe I could disappear. If I did Mom and Daddy could get back together and Matthew could grow up in a normal family. This isn't right. Something wrong. Something will happen. I know it will.

Tonight when Daddy came and stood in my bedroom door I thought something really bad was going
to happen. But it didn't. He just stood there smoking
his cigarette. I couldn't see his face--the light was
behind him. He was just a shadow, a big shadow
looming in my door.

I heard Mom's voice calling from their bedroom,
"Clifford! Clifford, could you come help me please."
Daddy said "Yeah, be right there." But he just stood
there, smoking, looking. I knew he was looking even
though I couldn't see his face. I pulled the covers up
to my chin and shut my eyes as tightly as possible. I
tried to breathe as if I were asleep. After a long time
he left without saying a word.

He thinks something is going to happen too. I can
tell he is worried. He probably can read my mind.
Sometimes I know I can read his.

ॐ 9 am, Sept 10 At home ॐ

I almost think I can see a puzzled smile on Elizabeth's
face. I'm not supposed to be here in my room at 9

o'clock on a Friday morning. I'm supposed to be at school. Elizabeth is shocked. What's going on here?

It's simple, Lizzie, I woke up sick this morning and Mom said I could stay home. I threw up as soon as I woke up. I think I was sick before I woke up. I was dreaming about being sick. I could feel myself wanting to throw up before I was awake.

I don't know why Mom was up, but she was. She heard me in the bathroom and came in and said I had stomach flu and had better stay home. Daddy didn't say anything to me all morning. He looked tired, but he went to work early. Mom brought me breakfast in bed --just some toast and hot tea, but it tasted good. I just finished it. Mom said she would put some sheets on the sofa in the family room so that I could watch TV while I was resting. I hope there's something good on.

---

3 pm, Sept 10
Aunt Rose's house

This may be the end of my diary.

I don't know what's going to happen now. It's terrible, worse than it was. Everything is worse. I may die soon. I don't know what will happen to me. I wish I hadn't done it. I wish I could keep my mouth shut. I wish I didn't cry so easily or show my feelings so much. I've ruined it. I've ruined everything. Daddy is gone. I think he's with the police, maybe in jail. I don't know what they are going to do to him. Whatever they do to him they'll probably do to me or worse. It's my fault, I know it is.

But the woman on TV...

The woman on TV said it wasn't her fault and she was glad she finally told. I think she must be crazy. Or I'm crazy.

I wish I hadn't turned on that program. I don't know why I did. I like the other shows better, but it came on and I was lying there on the sofa, and I just didn't get up to change the channel. And the announcement said the guest today was an incest victim, and she was going to talk about her ordeal, and I just froze there. I couldn't take my eyes off the TV. I didn't even notice Mom came in and stood in the doorway, watching too.

The woman on TV said it started when she was eight
and she would crawl into her Dad's bed on cold
nights because her room didn't have enough heat-
ing. She liked it then. It was warm and comfortable
and good to be hugged by your Dad. But then
things began to change.

I sat up on the sofa. Daddy's voice vibrated in my
head, "Hey, little doll, scared? Crawl in here. Come
on." And I did, because of the nightmares.

The nightmares started when Mom took classes at the
community college. They were good classes; they
were going to help Mom be a manager and not just a
waitress. But they meant she would be gone when I
went to bed every Monday, Wednesday and Friday.
"Don't wait up for me," she said to me. "Get to sleep.
Daddy's here. I'll see you in the morning."

But I couldn't sleep when she was gone. When
I dozed off I dreamed someone was shooting my
Mom. (Daddy said, "It's a bad area--where that
college is. Lots of pimps and thugs down there. I
wouldn't go near it especially if I was a woman, if you
know what I mean.") Or I lay awake looking at the
scary shadows on my ceiling and thought I saw
monsters--horrible creatures with long tentacles

reaching out to squeeze the breath out of me. I would jump up and run into Daddy's room. He was always awake, waiting for me. I often complained about Mom being gone, and he complained too. He told me when I got married I should stay home with my husband. He could show me how a husband liked to be treated, he said.

The woman on TV...

She said her father made her promise not to tell her mother. She was afraid to tell her mother, she said.

And Daddy...

After he started coming into my room on nights Mom was gone, he made me promise to keep our secret. It was just for us, he said. A special secret. I liked secrets, didn't I? I did.

The woman on TV introduced her friend, the woman she lived with. They talked about their life together. The other woman told about the time the first woman told her secret, told about her father molesting her.

It was when the first woman was 25 years old, and it was the first time she had ever told anyone. The interviewer said, "Twenty-five years old? You kept that ... terrible secret locked up inside you until you were twenty-five years old?" He seemed quite amazed and concerned. The woman began to get a little upset, and her friend patted her on the shoulder and calmed her. The woman told about her life since then, how things were better since she told, how people should tell someone if this happened to them, how she got help from a therapist, how she learned it was not her fault, she was not to blame.

I didn't realize I was crying until Mom said, "Here, honey, I'll turn this off..." She reached for the knob but I hear myself scream, "No!" And Mom just froze. She didn't turn her head to me at all. She just watched the woman on TV, and her hand slowly came off the knob. When a commercial came on she finally turned and looked at me. There were tears coming out of her eyes too. She just looked at me, and more tears came, and I began to sob, and a jingle about shampoo came on very loud on the TV. It was really strange--that happy shampoo song and both of us crying. Mom was kneeling on the floor; I was sitting on the sofa. We just cried for a while.

Then I stopped. I pulled the sheet up over my face, dried my cheeks, breathed slowly through the cool sheet. Mom turned off the TV. I liked the cool sheet

on my face and the darkness and the silence after
the TV was off. Mom didn't say a word.

That's when I realized: she knew all about it. She was
a part of it. She helped him do it. She wanted him to
do it.

"You know about me and Daddy," I said.

"What? No, I...It's just so sad, that woman--"

"What about me?" I yelled. "What about me?"

"Brenda, I don't..."

"You know! You knew all along."

"Knew? What...Brenda..." She was shaking her head.
She looked frightened. She was still kneeling on the
floor, and I was standing by now, screaming at her.
She seemed to think I was going to hit her. She put
her hands up as if to protect her head. Her eyes
pleaded, she had trouble getting her breath. She
didn't say a word, just shook her head, staring at me
as if I were a stranger.

I must have been. I certainly wasn't myself, not the
same good little doll I had always been with her and
Daddy. I was actually screaming at her, "You knew!

Why didn't you stop him?" She shook her head, shook her head, shook her head until she couldn't hold her head up anymore. She bowed her head low and shivered.

"I didn't know," she said. "I suspected something was wrong. Something...but nothing like that. I didn't, Brenda, I didn't know. I did try to talk to him... I tried...but he wouldn't...he just...wouldn't."

The room got so quiet then. It was like a tomb and I was the corpse. I was dead and I was still a child and I had never lived but now it was too late. I was dead. There was no crying or screaming anymore. It was still and finished. All over. Then I felt my legs moving under me. I was surprised they moved at all. I thought I couldn't move. I thought I was dead. But I did move. I stood up. I was like a movie camera that was walking. I could see the door and Mom's face sliding off to my right, and then the door got bigger and suddenly I was through it, in the living room, looking at the sofa and the sofa seemed to look at me--it was a stranger, and then it was an old friend, and all of a sudden there was another door, the front door, and I was making it open somehow, and it went around me, and I was outside. And I heard Mom's voice far off behind me somewhere, "Brenda,

where are you going?" she said. "Come back.
You're sick. You shouldn't go out sick."

I am sick. I ruined a family and Mom let me. I am
writing this in the guest bedroom of my Aunt Rose's
house. She's Mom's aunt actually, my great aunt.
But I've always called her Aunt. She's not much older
than Mom. She called Mom as soon as I came here.
She and Mom have been talking on the phone a lot
the last two days, but Mom hasn't come over yet,
and I only talked to her on the phone long enough to
tell her I was okay. I don't want to talk to her right
now. I don't want to talk to anyone right now.

Just now I heard Aunt Rose on the phone to Mom
asking her, "Did he admit it to the police?" I didn't
hear Mom's answer, but I peeked in and saw Rose
shaking her head as she listened. "What's going to
happen now, Martha?" she asked in a low voice.
When she heard the answer she shook her head
slowly again and began to rub the middle of her
forehead with her middle finger--the way she did at
Uncle Jim's funeral.

What's going to happen to my Daddy? Why can't I
see him at least? And tell him I'm sorry...or something. What's going to happen to me?

I wonder about my room at home and Elizabeth. Mrs. Bitterman from the Child Welfare office said they would go to my house, the police and someone from her office. Will they find them? All my little folded-up secret notes I wrote when I was seven and eight and nine? Will they find them? I had a dream last night that a big police interrogator had all my secret notes wadded up in his fist and he was hitting Daddy with that fist, making him tell too. They probably found them. They probably threw Elizabeth on my bed and took off her head and arms so they could get inside her and find all my little folded-up secret notes.

They are not going to find this, though. I'm going to take all these pages out of the notebook and hide them somewhere.

This is the end of my diary. I'm not going to write or tell anything more about myself.

It's too dangerous.

Second Diary

❧ 6 pm, Nov 17 Home ❧

Hey, Susan Fogelman...Hi!

I hate diaries that start out Dear Diary. Sounds dumb.

This time I'm typing my diary--as you will notice--
because I want it to be neater than the old one. The
old one was handwritten on notebook paper. I have
very neat handwriting, but the old diary was still kind
of messy. Messy and awful. Well, you know what it
was about, Susan. I've told you all that stuff.

Anyway, I want this diary to be neat and clean, the
way my life is now since Daddy left. I know you
wanted to read the old diary, Susan, but I really don't
want to dig it out and go through all those bad
memories again. I've gone through those things
three times now--once when they were actually
happening to me, a second time when I wrote about
them in my old diary, a third time when I talked with
you about my life. One thing I want to say, Susan, is
that I think you are an excellent therapist. You have
helped me so much, and I am so grateful to you. I
know I could not have gotten through these last two
months without you.

Well, you asked me to write down my thoughts and feelings about my life now. Actually things are going pretty well now, considering. It did help me to talk over everything with you, Susan, but now I really think it's time I put it all behind me and started making a whole new life for myself.

Oh, sure, problems still come up now and then. But that's to be expected, isn't it? I mean I still have a problem with Matthew, but Matthew and I were never close anyway. I don't know...he still acts like I ruined his life. At one time I thought that too. But you've helped me realize it wasn't my fault. Mom too--she makes me feel guilty if I let her. But I'm trying not to let her. Of course she helps me too. She's actually the one that talked me into coming to see you for the first time. And she wants to help; she really does. It's just very difficult for her. She loved Daddy--or needed him. Now he's so far away she doesn't know what to do with her love and her need. They are like chains around her neck. I know--I'm the same way. In spite of everything, I worry about him and wonder what he's doing.

But I've got to just forget all that and forge ahead. That's what Aunt Rose says--forge ahead. She doesn't like to talk about Daddy at all. She says

she'd like to kill him. I don't think she means that.
Do you?

Fortunately no one at school knows about the incest.
They just think Mom and Daddy are separated.
Almost all of my friends' parents are separated or
divorced. I have quite a few friends at school--not
really close friends, but people who know my name
and always speak to me. I wouldn't want them to
know about Daddy and me. They wouldn't understand. Like when my cousin Marsha found out (she's
Aunt Rose's granddaughter) she kind of freaked out
and she can't even seem to look at me straight
anymore. If I catch her looking at me she'll look
away suddenly as if she wasn't supposed to even
look at me. I think she's afraid to touch me too--like I
had a contagious disease or something. But I don't.
Do you think everyone my age would react the same
way? The reason I ask is because there is one person
I might have to tell someday. I mean, if I got married,
would my husband be able to tell I was sexually
molested by my father? Don't worry--I know I'm too
young to get married right now, but I was just
wondering.

I guess I better sign off now and do my homework.
By the way, I have A's in all my classes, and I've made
up all my work from the time I missed in September.

🐦 6 pm, Nov 24 Home 🐦

Hi, Susan.

It's nice knowing who's going to read this. Before, I didn't know if anyone would ever read what I was writing in my diary. I guess I didn't really want anyone to read it. I just wanted to say it, I guess.

Now I know you're going to read it, and that's much better, because I know you won't put me down or try to make me feel bad about the things I say. Like the way you answered all my questions from the first journal entry. You really do listen, and you really do try to answer my questions. No one has ever really done that before--no adult anyway. I do have this friend at school, you know. I told you about him. He listens to me.

Scott really does seem to want to know me better. He says he does. He calls me on the phone every day. I see him every day at lunch. He wants me to go to a rock concert with him Saturday, I don't know ...if Daddy was still at home he would say no. He thought rock concerts were just big teen-age orgies. I don't think so. Do you?

You told me if Scott and I got married he wouldn't necessarily be able to tell if I had been sexually abused. But if I wasn't able to have sex...if I got scared or started remembering about Daddy's abuse that could be a problem. I wonder if I shouldn't try to face up to it now. Maybe I should tell Scott. I don't think he would freak out the way Marsha did or clam up like Matthew. But what would he think of me? Would he think something was wrong with me? He might not want a girl that had already been messed over. But you told me I was already physically okay, I just had to make sure my thinking was okay too.

I'm trying hard to think the right thing. I know what you said is true--that I am not spoiled or ruined by the abuse. I'm just me, a 15-year old girl who had all these things done to her by someone who should have helped and protected her instead of hurting her. And I know I'm not bad; I'm not to blame. I was a victim. Was a victim. Now I'm trying to be a survivor. And I think I'm going to succeed.

I also think I can make Scott understand all this. I really think I can.

❧ 3 pm, Nov 26 Home ❧

Dear Susan:

I'm putting this on stationery (Isn't it pretty? Scott
gave it to me for my birthday.) because I am going
to mail this, and my latest journal entry, to you. You
see, I think I am going to drop out of the sessions for
now--both my individual time and the group sessions.
I really think it's time I did this. I know you think I
should continue, but I really don't think I want to. I
can see that most of those other girls probably need
to stay in the group therapy a while longer. Most of
them had an even worse time of it than I did and still
need to talk about their problems some more. I don't
think I do.

For one thing we have talked a lot about the incest
already--it really has helped. But I do want to get on
with my life and try to leave that behind me. I don't
think it's going to do any good to keep talking about
Daddy. I mean he's not here anymore, and he
doesn't molest me anymore. What's the good of
dragging it all up again?

One thing you may or may not realize is that I still love

Daddy in a way. At least I think I do. Anyway I feel something for him. I can't quite understand what my feelings are, but I know when we talk about him it makes me very nervous. Or sometimes I get a really bad stomach ache like a great big hand is reaching down inside me and tearing out my insides.

I don't want to put myself through that anymore. So I think it's time I stopped the therapy, even though it has been very, very helpful to me.

One of the things that has been most helpful to me is talking to the other girls in the group--or rather listening to them, since I haven't talked too much in there since that first session. I always thought I was the only one who had this problem, this kind of family. I couldn't imagine that in all those nice, normal-looking families I saw all around me there might be other fathers molesting their children. One of the girls in the group, Sally, lives on South Adams Street, just around the corner from us. I've walked by there a million times. I would never have thought anything like that could happen in their family. I never imag-ined that anything like that could happen in any-body's family except mine. I thought I was alone and had to deal with my special problem all by myself. You, and all the other girls in the group, have made me realize I'm not alone. Others have survived. I can survive too. I will survive.

Right now I just want to live as normal a life as possible. I have an idea in my mind--it's a composite of all those living rooms I've peeked into in my neighborhood. It's a family, just settling into evening activities as dusk settles in too. It's comfortable. Everyone is relaxed. People laugh, smile, hug, talk. It's a family, a real family. Everyone is happy. I want that for me.

Sincerely,

Brenda

❧ *Midnight, Nov 26 My room* ❧

Susan, something happened tonight. I need to tell someone. But everyone is asleep except me.

And Elizabeth.

Elizabeth...

It's you and me again.

You're the only one who stays the same. You're the only one who doesn't hurt. I can count on you. Always there, never blinking, always pretty, always smiling, always perfect, peaceful and alone.

I can look at you and almost forget...

I can sit here on this bed and look at your face that looks at the wall and not have to think...

I can close my eyes and still see your face and not have to dream...

Maybe if I can keep your face in mind I will be able to get to sleep, and I will wake in the morning and this will all be over, all forgotten...

A bad dream fading in the light of morning...

A bad smell dispersing...

Bourbon.

As soon as I smelled it on him I recognized the smell.

Remembered it.

Daddy drank bourbon at Christmas. It's sweet and vinegary and woody on someone's breath. I don't know what it tastes like from a glass or bottle. But I can't get the smell or taste out of me. I have gargled, brushed my teeth, sprayed the air freshener in my room. It's in my head. Bourbon in my head. Awful, sweet, sickening bourbon.

Scott.

I have written his name like that a hundred times-- on test papers, magazine pages, inside my notebook, on a secret page of my Biology book. I've always crossed it through if I thought anyone would see it later. I just liked to write it.

Scott.

He came to get me tonight at 6:30. We went to Maria's Restaurant for pizza. It's where all the kids from our school go on Friday nights. I never used to get to go when Daddy was home. Now Mom lets me go with Scott every Friday night. Usually a large group of kids from school sit at the big tables and make a lot of noise. Scott and I sit by ourselves and just talk. We sometimes stay a long time, not eating much, just sitting and talking. They don't seem to mind.

Tonight Scott said, "You should eat more, Brenda. You hardly ever eat anything."

"I know," I said. "I'm too skinny. Daddy says I should eat more--" It just slipped out. I hadn't meant to mention Daddy. Suddenly I couldn't think of anything to say. I sipped my drink. Scott sipped his.

"You hear anything from your Dad?" he said.

"No, not much," I said and sipped some more.

"Your Mom and Dad still getting divorced?"

"Mmm." I nodded my head, still sipping, though I was not really swallowing anything.

"That's too bad," he said, stirring the ice in his cup.

"Yeah." I stirred the ice in my cup.

"My folks have been split up three years now," he said. I stopped stirring and looked at him. He had never told me that. "Yeah," he said. "Phil is my stepfather."

"I didn't know that," I said.

"Yeah, most people don't. We have a really good relationship, Phil and I. We didn't at first though." He stopped his stirring and looked at me. We were quiet for a long time, looking at each other.

"Want to go for a ride?" he said.

"Sure."

We drove down to Bridle Park which is next to Brighton Town, the historic district where college kids and high school kids who look old enough to get into bars hang out. We just went for a walk in Bridle Park and talked some more about Scott's family, about his folks' divorce, and his stepfather. He didn't ask anything more about my family, and I didn't bring anything up.

I was really enjoying our conversation. It was so personal and friendly and open. It really seemed there were no secrets between us then. We were really friends, really sharing our thoughts and feelings

the way I always imagined friends were supposed to.
It reminded me of the talks I had had with Susan
during my individual sessions. I have never had a
really close relationship like that with someone my
own age. When I was little, Great Grandmother and I
talked like this, I think, but that was long ago. A few
times Mom and I talked well, but never for very long.

I really thought it was wonderful, strolling in Bridle Park
with the college students and my very own boyfriend,
talking about grown-up things without any fears or
secrets. I began to have visions of all the rest of my
life becoming something like this beautiful walk in the
park on a crisp, clear November night. I began to
envision Scott and me living in our neatly arranged,
softly lighted home, having conversations like this
every night while a small and beautiful child plays on
the rug nearby. A family machine, smooth-running,
relaxed, well-connected by love, oiled by care.

We finally stopped walking and sat on a park bench,
a little tired and quite relaxed. For some time we just
sat silently enjoying the cool air and the pleasant
sights.

"Why did your folks split up?" Scott asked out of the
clear blue. He wasn't looking at me, just staring off at

the trees and the couples strolling by, but I felt eyes on me anyway. I felt as if part of my clothing had fallen off and other parts were loose and about to be blown off by the breeze. I shut my eyes, breathed very deeply and plunged in. I was afraid to wait too long.

"Yeah," I said, "that's something I've been wanting to tell you about." I paused to breathe carefully and heard my heart beating. I wasn't looking at him, but I knew Scott had turned to look at me. He didn't say anything.

Why am I nervous about this? I wondered. I've told other people. First, Mom, then Aunt Rose. Then Mrs. Bitterman from the Child Welfare office. I told Susan, of course, and all the girls in the group. I didn't tell Matthew, but we talked about it a little. For several weeks I have been planning to tell Scott. I knew the beautiful visions of Scott and me in the future depended on getting over this hurdle from my past. But what would he think? What would he say? I didn't blame him for his parents' split. How could he blame me? But, of course, this was different.

"What do you mean?" he asked at last.

"I..." Quickly turning to face him I took one of his
hands in both of mine and held on tightly. "Scott, he
molested me...my Daddy...my father...molested me."

Scott laughed. He thought I was joking. But then he
saw I wasn't. Then he didn't believe me. He just
shook his head and quit looking at me. "It's true," I
said. "It really is. It started when I was very young--
before I knew anything much about sex at all. I never
knew, never understood what he was doing to me
exactly. He just kept on. Finally I told. I'm getting
help now from a woman who's an expert about it. A
lot of people have had this problem, not just me."

"Well...why?" he finally said.

"I don't know."

"Naw," he said. "That doesn't make any sense at all.
He must have had some...There must have been
some reason...Maybe you dreamed something when
you were little."

"No. It was happening until three months ago," I said.

"But, Brenda, you couldn't...that couldn't be
something that could happen to you. I mean, you're
so smart and..."

"It has nothing to do with smart. I just didn't know," I said. Our voices were rising. We were arguing. He refused to believe me.

"Brenda, you're one of the prettiest...best dressed... most...poised girls in the whole school. You make straight A's! Why are you...? What are you trying to--?"

"I'm not making this up, Scott!" I screamed. "It really happened. It's really hard for me to tell you, but I wanted to tell you. I wanted you to know about me. I wanted us to be honest...I wanted us to be friends, real friends, not just friends to talk and eat pizza and say hello in the halls, but friends who could trust each other and help each other and not blame each other." I was crying so hard I didn't realize how loud my voice had gotten. A couple had stopped and turned toward us. I turned my face against the back of the bench. He stared at the ground. When the couple went on I said, "Let's go. Okay?"

We got up and hurried back to the car, both of us watching our feet walk. When we got in the car and shut the doors he said, "I've never heard of this, not...I don't know what to..." And he turned to look at me. But it was if my face was a bright light. He couldn't look at me very long without glancing away.

"Take me home. Okay, Scott?" I didn't recognize my own voice. It was like a child's voice. He drove me home without saying a word. As soon as the car stopped in front of my house I got out and ran inside. He didn't say anything, and I didn't either. I needed time alone to think and so did he, I suppose.

Mom wasn't home. She wasn't expecting me until 11:30, my curfew; so she had gone out for the evening. She usually went to the movies with Rose on Friday nights when I was out with Scott. I was glad she wasn't home tonight. It's nice sometimes not to have to worry if my radio was playing too loud or if I was doing something that would bother Mom. She is so nervous these days you have to be careful.

I turned on my radio and flopped on my bed. I let my shoes dangle off my feet then fall to the floor. I wanted to lose myself in the music. Usually I can do that, and it helps. I didn't want to think about Scott just then, not yet. I was afraid I had made a mistake. I was afraid we might not be able to keep going together, and I didn't want to face up to that just yet. I didn't want to think at all. I just wanted to listen. Drifting along on a good song, following the tune wherever it leads, riding off on the beat to a faraway dream, I could forget who I was, where I was, where I had been.

I guess that's why I didn't hear Scott knocking on the front door--the music was too loud, and I was in another world. Anyway, I guess he heard the music and knew I was there; and so he came on in (I probably forgot to push the door tight shut; so it wasn't locked).

I didn't know he had come into the house until he said, "Brenda?" I sat up quicker than anything and saw right away who it was, even though I only had the reading lamp on in my room, and he was kind of silhouetted in my bedroom door.

"Scott?" I said.

"Yeah," he said and just stood there. I turned the radio off.

"You scared me," I said.

He seemed to nod his head, but I couldn't see any expression on his face. "I knocked, but I guess you didn't hear."

"No. I've been lying here listening to the radio ever since you brought me home. What have you been doing?"

"I went over to Buddy's." I was thinking how different his voice sounded when he suddenly explained why that was so, "We had a couple of shots of bourbon."

"Oh." I knew Buddy was his friend, two years older, already in college, living in his own apartment. "Why'd you do that?" I asked.

"I don't know," he said and put his hands in his pockets. I knew he hated liquor. He had just told me tonight about his real father's drinking problem. He hated it. He hated drunks. "I'm not drunk," he said. "Just a couple."

I stood up and went toward him. "You want a coke or something?" I said. I was wanting to go into the living room and sit down. I didn't like him standing there in my doorway the way Daddy used to.

"I wanted to tell you something," he said, without budging. I couldn't get past him. He blocked the doorway.

"What?" I said.

"I had sex with Kelly Brandon once."

I sat back down on the bed. "Why did you tell me that?" I said.

"You told me your sexual experience. I thought I should tell you mine."

I nodded my head but couldn't say anything. He came and sat down beside me on the bed. He moved closer, and I didn't move at all. Doll babies only move when someone moves them. He turned my head toward him and began to kiss me. I could smell his usual brand of shampoo and something else as well. The bourbon was sweet and vinegary and woody on his lips and made his kisses seem different.

Daddy at Christmas.

Mom went to visit Rose and stayed a long time. Why wouldn't she come back? Why wouldn't Daddy leave me alone? And he smelled so awful.

"I hate that smell of bourbon," I said.

"I'm sorry," he mumbled, still kissing me. "I was pretty upset." He put his hands on my shoulders and very firmly pushed me back so I was lying across the bed. He leaned over me. I looked up automatically at

Elizabeth. She was sitting up there as usual, staring peacefully at the wall, doing nothing, just like me. Doll baby, do this, doll baby, do that. I couldn't smell anything but bourbon. I thought it was Christmas. I thought he was Daddy. I thought I was suffocating.

"Get up," I said. "Get off me."

"Why?"

"We shouldn't do this. I don't want to do this now."

"Why not? You've done it before, haven't you? Why not?" He wouldn't get up.

"I've done it..." I started, but I felt a great sob coming up from the middle of my body. I tried to stop myself from crying or growling or whatever was coming out of me. I tried to speak again, "I've done it...I've done...what he said...done...done...done..." My body heaved with sobs and my mouth opened wide but not a sound came out. The sound was there, I felt it, but it was stuck somewhere, held somewhere. Scott jumped up immediately. I must have had a horrible look on my face. He looked scared, really scared. I stood up, still heaving with a sob that wouldn't come out. Finally I screamed, growled, made a sound of some kind. It was a terrible sound. Scott backed up into my dresser. A photograph fell off. He didn't pick it up.

"I hate him," I yelled. "Hate him! Hate him! Hate him!"

"Brenda, I'm sorry, I--"

"Hate him. He hurt me, wouldn't let me up, hurt me. Hate him...hate him..." I sat back down and cried into my hands. When I stopped and looked up, Scott was in the doorway, just standing there. I couldn't look at him. It was Daddy, standing there looking at me.

"Brenda, I'm sorry...I...I'm going home, Brenda. I'm sorry."

By the time I looked again he was gone. I didn't hear his footsteps or the door shut or anything. He just disappeared. Did I dream all that?

No, the photograph he knocked off still lay on the floor. I put it back in its place. I like everything to be exactly in its place in my room. I began to straighten things up, but there was nothing else to straighten once the photograph was replaced. I was left with

nothing to do with my hands, and I wanted something to do with my hands, something to do.

I can't remember ever feeling this way. I'm not the
kind of person who gets mad. I never get mad. I
screamed at Scott and scared him. I scared myself.
What's happening to me? Things were going so well
and then wham! It's all bad again.

It's Daddy. He's still here like a ghost. A ghost in my
head. When I think about it...all those years...I want
to throw something, break something. But I can't. I
don't do that sort of thing. I've got to do something.
I've written all this--Susan, you said it would help to
write things down when they bothered me. I think I'm
going to call you. I have your number. You said
call if I needed to.

I need to.

Third Diary

9 am, Jan 1 Home

This is a new diary. I still have the old ones--the one
on looseleaf notebook paper; and the neatly type-
written one, the one I took in to show Susan. But this
one is different from both of those. This diary is a
bound book. On the front it says "My Journal" and
has a place to write your name and the date. I did
that, even though I think it's kind of corny. It's a nice-
looking journal with gold embossed letters on a brown
leather-like cover. It won't be easy--and would look
messy--to tear out these pages; so I will have to say
what I mean the first time and let it go at that.

I will try to do that. I will try to write down the truth as I
see it, and then I will stand by it. This will be my record
--my own record and no one else's--of my survival.
And I am surviving. It is not easy, but I believe I will
continue to survive and will perhaps come out with a
better life. If you knew me in person, you might not
find me as confident as I seem here, but here is where
I am beginning to learn to have confidence. Here is
where I am beginning to become myself.

After that night with Scott (It was only five weeks ago-
it seems years) I called Susan and told her I wanted

to come back to therapy sessions. She said she was glad to hear that. She also said the other girls in the group had asked about how I was doing. I can't describe the warmth I felt talking to Susan on the phone. Like a dozen gentle hands touching my back and shoulders and head and face. And I relaxed more deeply than I had in a long time.

I am still troubled--there is so much still wrong in this house, this family, in me. But no one's life is perfect, and the important thing for me right now is that I have a place to go. A safe place. A helping place.

ᘛ 4 pm, Jan 12 Home ᘚ

Susan took me to her doctor--Doctor Bradley--because I didn't want our family doctor to know about Daddy. At first I didn't want any doctor to know about it, I didn't want to talk to a doctor at all. Back in September when I first started talking to Susan she tried to get me to have a physical exam, but I wouldn't do it. I was afraid. I was afraid the doctor might find something really bad wrong with me. I was afraid of what they would think of me--the doctor, the nurse, the receptionist, the other people in the waiting room. Would the other people know why I was there? I had thought maybe I could cough a lot and pretend I had a bad cold. I still worry about things like that. I know I shouldn't, but I do.

Doctor Bradley was very nice. Susan told him what I was concerned about, and then he asked me a few questions and examined me. It didn't take long at all, and afterwards he invited me and Susan to come into his office.

He told us a funny story about when he was an intern and someone switched his name tag with the head nurse's name tag. He didn't know about the switch until someone called him Betty (that was the nurse's name). Doctor Bradley laughed even more at the story than we did. He had a big jolly laugh.

He showed us a picture of his family--his wife, a son who was in college, and a daughter still in high school. Finally he asked me if I had any questions.

I said I didn't, but I really did have a few questions. He said if I ever wanted to ask him anything, just to call his number, and he would either talk to me then or call me back when he was free. I said I would. I thought to myself that I should write down my questions so I wouldn't waste any of his time.

"Basically," he said, "you are a healthy young woman.
The sexual abuse you suffered has not left you physically injured or sexually damaged in the physical sense.
Your hymen is not intact now as it was when you were
a small child, but that does not impair you in any way,
and it is not an injury really. It is simply the normal
consequence of the vagina being penetrated--
whether by sexual intercourse or some other physical
intrusion into the vagina. Do you understand?"

I nodded yes.

"Good," he said and picked up the chart that had
my name on it. "Now, just looking at you, and looking
at your weight here, I wonder how your appetite is."

"Not too great," I said. "I get sick at my stomach
pretty easily--not as much now as I used to. Now I
usually eat the most at lunch. We have a good
lunchroom at school."

"Well, you're a little underweight, I guess," he said,
"but maybe you'll just become a model and get
paid for it."

I smiled, and he laughed his big laugh and stood up. Susan and I got up too and thanked him and left. In Susan's car on the way back I asked her if it was possible to get pregnant from incest, and she said it was possible.

"But you're not, Brenda, you're fine."

We talked about pregnancy and birth control and a bunch of things. It was the most grown-up conversation I've ever had. Once Mom and I talked about sex, but I could tell Mom didn't enjoy talking about it. Susan didn't seem to mind. It was just like talking about the weather with her. She answered any question I asked and tried to explain everything as clearly and honestly as possible.

I said, "I guess I wonder about these things so much because I've been sexually abused."

"No," she said. "Everybody wonders about these things, especially at your age. It's quite normal." Then she looked right at me. "You're a fine, healthy young woman, Brenda."

We rode a long time in silence before I asked her, "Do you think I could really get paid to be a model?"

"I don't know," she said. "I've heard it's a very tough business. But you are certainly pretty enough."

"I'm plenty skinny enough," I said, "but I don't think I have good enough bone structure."

"What? You have beautiful bone structure, perfect bone structure. I wish I had your bone structure."

I was stunned by this news. I just looked at her. She glanced at me and nodded as if to say, "Yes, I mean it."

Again we drove in silence for a while. I thought she was concentrating on her driving--traffic was heavy-- so I didn't think she would notice my pulling down a visor in front of me. There was a little mirror on the back of it with a cover. I lifted the cover and looked at myself in the mirror. I looked for a long time from all different angles. After a while it seemed as if I were looking at someone else, a perfect stranger, a pretty stranger, perhaps a model.

Suddenly I realized we were stopped at a stop light. I looked over at Susan. She was looking right at me, smiling, her eyes twinkling. I blushed like a tomato, closed the mirror cover and pushed the visor up.

I looked back at Susan. She was still looking, still smiling, still twinkling. I started to smile myself, and that made Susan laugh. Pretty soon I was laughing too. And we just sat there laughing until the light changed and the man behind us honked his horn. That made us laugh even more, but Susan did manage to get the car going and through the intersection.

I have never known a grown-up like Susan. She knows a lot, and she is fun to be around. She listens to me, really listens, and never puts me down. I used to think my doll Elizabeth was the only thing I could count on, the only thing I could trust, in this world. But now I think I can trust Susan.

❧ 7 pm, Jan 19 Home ❧

Today Mom came with me to see Susan. She came one time before, but she got so upset she didn't want to come back, even though Susan kept asking her to come. Yesterday I went to Mom myself and said "Please come with me. Susan says it will help us both, and I think so too."

She looked at me, a little surprised. I don't think she

was expecting me to ask her directly. "All right," she
said, "if you really want me to."

"I do, Mom."

So today we both went in, and Susan was very gra-
cious and tried to make Mom feel comfortable. But
Mom wouldn't even take her coat off. "It's a little
chilly in here," she explained, and Susan didn't mention it again.

At first Mom wouldn't talk to me directly. I think she
thought: Susan is the therapist, we should talk to her.
But Susan explained it was fine--in fact, better--for us
to talk directly to each other.

"Well," Mom said, still not looking at me, "I know
Brenda has been through a lot. It's been very hard
on her...hard on all of us...very hard. But still we have
to keep on. We have to do our jobs and take care of
things."

"That's very true," Susan said. I nodded in agreement,
and Susan asked, "Did you have something specific
in mind, something that needs taking care of?"

"Well," Mom said, "I was just thinking in general. But there is a little problem in the mornings." She looked up at Susan, who said, "Go on." Mom still didn't look at me, but she went on, "Well, in the mornings Brenda has always helped out, because I work late at the restaurant. She used to always make breakfast for Matthew and help him get ready for school. She used to be a regular little mother in the mornings, and it really helped out. Now she doesn't want to do that anymore, she doesn't want to help. Why doesn't she? Is she mad at me or something?"

"Why don't you ask her," Susan said.

Mom looked at me, looked down, rubbed her ring finger the way I had seen her do so many times, and finally said very quietly, "Are you mad at me, Brenda?"

I didn't answer. I was afraid of what I might say. Susan asked, "You don't want to make breakfast for Matthew anymore, Brenda?"

"No," I said and glanced at Mom. She was listening.

"And you don't want to help him get dressed?"

"No," I said.

"Why not?" Susan said gently.

"Because Matthew hates me," I blurted.

"He does not," Mom said.

"Yes, he does, Mom," I said. "He thinks it's all my fault. He thinks I made it up."

"I've explained to him--" Mom started, but I couldn't stop: "He thinks I just wanted to get rid of Daddy because he wouldn't let me go out at night. He thinks I should say it was all a lie; so Daddy could come back home. He says the kids at school say things to him, and it's all my fault. He won't do anything I tell him, he won't even answer me when I ask him a question. He's terrible to me, and I'm tired of it."

There was a long silence while Mom rubbed her ring finger. I thought Susan might say something, but she didn't. She just watched. Finally Mom said, "For a long time, Brenda, Matthew has thought you were keeping him away from his father. I tried to explain to him it was not your fault, it was his father's fault. It's hard for him to accept. He told me...he said once... that sometimes he wished Daddy would let you go out and make him stay at home; so they could talk. It's hard on him. A boy needs a father, I guess..."

"He needs a mother too," I said.

"What do you mean?" Mom asked.

"I mean you're Matthew's mother. You should be there in the mornings too. I don't mind helping. I don't mind cooking breakfast, helping out, but I think you should be there too. Matthew needs his mother too."

Mom nodded. "I know, Brenda. I should...it's just so hard to take all that crap at the restaurant at night and then bounce up bright and early in the mornings and be a great mother. Some mornings I just can't face it."

"You don't have to be a 'great' mother, Mom," I said. "Just be there. That's enough for me. You could go back to bed after we go to school."

Mom smiled. "I guess Matthew does need more of a mother."

I nodded my head. Susan said in her gentle voice,

"And what about you, Brenda? Do you need more of a mother too?"

"Yes," I said, but they didn't hear me.

"What, Brenda?" Susan asked.

I looked up straight at Mom. "Yes," I said again. I could see tears just forming in Mom's eyes. It was like the time we saw the TV program on incest and we knew each other's thoughts. "I need a mother too," I went on, "someone who will take care of me and help me and protect me."

"And I didn't," Mom said. "I know I didn't. I wish I had. I wish I could have been sure, Brenda. I wish I had listened to my hunches. I wish...so much..."

Mom cried easily now, and so did I. Susan said, "The past is over, but what can we do about the future?"

Mom said, "I can promise you I will try to help you through this. I'll do...whatever I can do...and I'll do my best to protect you when I can...when I know."

"Good," Susan said.

"Thank you, Mom," I said.

"And I can tell you I'm sorry. I'm sorry it happened.
I just didn't know...I didn't know how to protect you.
I didn't understand the risk, Brenda. I just thought--
I assumed--you were safe with your Daddy. Any
mother would, wouldn't she? I just assumed we
could trust him, both of us. I just assumed...but I was
wrong. I know. Now I know, Brenda. I know better,
and I'm sorry."

She put her arms around me, and I hugged her too.
We held on tight and cried together and then were
quiet together for a long time, still holding on to each
other.

❧ 8 pm, Jan 26 Home ❧

Today in the group session I finally told them about
Scott and what happened that night he drank the
bourbon. It was the most I had ever said at the group
session, and I was amazed at how closely they all
listened to me. They seemed to be genuinely interested in what I had to say. I've always hesitated to

say much in the group for fear of boring them. But they weren't bored at all. After I finished speaking they started asking questions and some began telling about things that had happened to them that were a lot like what happened to me.

Sandy said a whole group of boys found out about her sexual abuse, and every time she got near one of those boys he would begin to make suggestive remarks and ask if she would like to have sex since she was so experienced. She finally transferred to another school district.

Patty told us she did the opposite thing--she followed boys around and tried to get them interested in her. She had sex with several boys and felt worse each time. Finally she was thinking about suicide and decided to come back to the group. She realized now, she said, that she was wanting to be loved, that she was wanting to prove that even though she was an incest victim she was still lovable.

Carmen, the oldest one in our group, told her, "Don't be an incest victim, Patty; be an incest survivor."

"Yeah," someone else said, and several heads nodded in agreement.

Tiffany, the only girl in the group quieter than me, spoke up next and said she was afraid she would never be able to have sex with a man. She couldn't bear the thought of it, she said.

"Me too," someone else said.

"Maybe you'll change," another person suggested.

"I don't know," Tiffany said. "Maybe. The thing is I don't want a man, but I do want children. I love children, and I think I could do a good job of raising children."

"You could adopt kids," someone suggested.

We talked about children for a while, about being children and about having children. Susan talked about children's rights. Then we talked more about being survivors rather than victims.

It was one of the best group sessions I've been to. It's terrific the way we can talk so freely in that group. We can talk about anything and say what we really think and feel. I've always been afraid to join in groups at school. I was afraid of what I might reveal about myself. Here we already know the worst about each other; so we're free to try to find something better in each other.

I don't know why I left this group and Susan. I guess I thought I had taken care of all my problems and wanted to forget about them. But really I hadn't faced up to all my problems yet, and trying to forget about bad things in your life can make those things even worse.

There have been several who dropped out. A few of us have come back. I wonder about the others who haven't come back. I think they should consider coming back. I am really glad I did.

❧ 4 pm, Feb 11 Home ❧

I signed up to be on the make-up crew for the Spring play at school. The play is "You Can't Take It With You". Scott is in it and a girl I sit by in Science. I think it will be fun, and I'm very interested in make-up. I'm fascinated by the way a little bit of make-up can change a person's whole appearance.

❧ 6 pm, Feb 23 Home ☙

Matthew has been coming to the Center for therapy and today we were in a session together. I think we are finally beginning to work out some of our problems at home.

❧ 10 pm, Feb 25 Home ☙

I try not to, but I can't help it--I keep thinking about Daddy, wondering what he's doing, what he's feeling. I wonder if he thinks about me. I wonder if he remembers. I do. I used to try not to remember everything, but now I just let it come into my head if it wants to. Sometimes they're good things, sometimes not so good. I never know what I'm going to remember or why, but I always remember something.

Tonight I was thinking about my music box. Daddy gave it to me for my sixth birthday. He got it at the Silver Bells Shop downtown and it was really expensive. I know that because he and Mom had a big fight about it. I wasn't supposed to hear them arguing, but I did. And I remember. I was just six, but I remember everything. Daddy always got me expensive presents for my birthday and Mom always thought he shouldn't have spent so much money. She didn't always say anything, but I could always tell she was mad about him spending so much money on me. I wonder if he did it because he felt guilty. Or was he trying to find a way to show he loved me?

Even then, even when I was six, things weren't right between us. I didn't know it at the time--or I didn't understand, but now, when I remember, I know things weren't right. Sometimes he held me so long and so tight I thought I couldn't breathe good, and I would have to get up and run outside until my face felt cool again. And sometimes he tickled my leg--not a big tickle to make you laugh, but a soft tickle, like a feather stroke over and over until I asked to do something else. They weren't big things, not bad things-- really it was just the way he did them. Sometimes I was scared, or just confused. I didn't know anything was wrong. I was just six, and it was my Daddy, and my Mom was there too, so I didn't say anything about being scared or confused. I just kept it all to myself. Until now.

The music box is so pretty. It has jewels on it. I guess they're not jewels but they look real. And it's painted white--shiny bright white and smooth as glass. The song it plays is "My Bonnie Lies Over the Ocean", and every time I hear it I think of Daddy. I like it so much because it makes me remember the good things.

I miss him. I wonder if I will see him again. I guess someday. He and Mom are getting divorced. Mom says it should be final by the end of the month. She doesn't say too much about him now.

---

9 pm, Mar 11   Home

Rehearsals began today for "You Can't Take It With You". Scott is the kindly old grandfather, and Barbara, my friend in Science class, plays a really kookie lady, which is a perfect part for her, because she is really kookie in everyday life.

---

10 pm, Apr 2   Home

I haven't been writing much in my journal because I have been so busy with working on the play. I am now on the set construction crew too because a couple of the kids on that crew got bad grades at the quarter and had to drop out. I've been helping paint flats every afternoon after school--sometimes till 7:30 or 8. I don't mind doing it at all. It's great to help create something good, and I think this play will be excellent. It's all about a really weird but really nice family and another family that's not weird at all--in fact they're more real and quite funny and endearing. The whole play is extremely funny, but it's very warm too, and full of love.

🐚 1:30 am, Apr 16 My room 🐚

I'm exhausted! Tonight was opening night! And I went to the cast party! It's 1:30 right now, but I'm too excited to sleep; so I thought I would scribble a little. That always relaxes me.

First, I should tell you that the play went incredibly well. Mr. Ramirez, our principal, said it was the best play our school had ever put on. Of course, somebody said he said the same thing last year, but still I think he really liked it, and so did everyone else in the audience.

Scott and Barbara were terrific. They got the most laughs. Scott really makes an endearing old man.

Of course, I felt like I could take some credit for that
because I designed his make-up--and helped him
put it on too. He doesn't have a very steady hand
when it comes to drawing lines on his face.

After the play it was a madhouse backstage. It was
really exciting to be there and feel a part of the
whole thing. It took forever for people to get out of
costume and make-up, and all of us on the make-up
crew had to stay till the end because we have to
put up the make-up.

Scott was the last one to get out of his make-up, and
he asked me to help him get it off.

"You showed me how to put it on, but you didn't tell
me how to get it off," he said. "Maybe I should just
leave it on?"

"It looks nice if I do say so myself," I said. "But I think
you'd look pretty silly at the cast party."

"Yeah," he said and admired himself in the mirror.
I think he was reluctant to leave his role. Grandpa
is such a delightful and lovable character, I don't
blame him.

"Well, where do I start?" he said.

I dipped a big gob of cold cream and splatted it on his face. "With this stuff," I said. It made him laugh.

I showed him how to rub the cold cream into the make-up and loosen it from his face. "Now tissues," I said, and I showed him how to wipe off the whole mess. After he washed his face and washed the grey out of his hair in the lavatory, he came back and sat down at his place at the make-up mirror. I was sitting there too, putting up make-up. We looked at each other in the mirror. He looked like himself again.

"I liked myself better as an old man," he said.

"You did an excellent job," I said.

"Thanks." We continued to look at each other in the mirror. Finally he said, "I also liked myself better before that night...at your house."

I looked down at the make-up in my hands and remembered. I looked back at the mirror, and he was still looking steadily at my reflection. I met his eyes, and he said, "I was stupid. I didn't understand at all. I probably still don't. But I do understand how stupid I acted that night."

"I can forgive you," I said.

He looked at me a long time and then said "Thank you, Brenda."

I turned to look at the real face beside me, and he turned to look at mine.

"Need a ride to the cast party?" he said.

"I told Barbara I'd ride with her. You want to ride with us?"

"Yeah, thanks," he said.

I can't believe how loud and crazy that cast party was. There was a lot of good food, but it was mainly gone in the first ten minutes. The music was so loud you couldn't hear yourself think, let alone talk. Some of the kids were drinking booze outside, and I think a few were smoking pot somewhere. I was really glad to get back home.

It's so nice and quiet here in my room. Even with the window open, it's quiet. I guess everyone else in the neighborhood is asleep.

I love these first days of Spring when you can leave your windows open and listen to things going on outside and smell the flowers that are just beginning to bud. It's a wonderful, renewing time. The grass comes back, the jonquil flowers, the maple trees-- they all come back like old friends from summer vacation. Only theirs is a winter vacation. Now we are all back in the Spring and growing again.

On top of my chest of drawers Elizabeth sits and looks happy to have the Spring breeze blowing her way. But then she always looks happy. It's easy when the smile is painted on. Real smiles are a little harder to come by, but they're also better.

I'm smiling too right now, but I don't know why exactly. Maybe it's Spring Fever.

Considering all that's happened to me this year, and the past several years, maybe I don't have a reason to smile, but I am anyway. It's not a smile for what is past; so it must be a smile for what's to come. For the future.

Of course, I don't know what the future will be exactly, but I do know I will be facing it with some new confidence in myself and some new hope. And not as a victim, but a survivor.

Elizabeth, you're a survivor too. You've passed through three generations to me, and, if I someday have a daughter, I will pass you on to her.

That's not all I will pass on to her. I think I will also pass on the things I've learned this year. That will be an even better gift than this beautiful old doll.

I can see her now in my mind's eye: my daughter. She is pretty and smiling like you, Elizabeth, because she is loved and knows she is protected and respected. Perhaps she is even named after you, Elizabeth.

Dear little Elizabeth, my daughter to be...I don't know what the world will be like when you come to live upon it, but I think you will still need to know these things I have learned. You will need to know that even when you are small you have rights just like grown-ups...

You have the right to be yourself, a child.

You have the right to be nourished and protected physically and emotionally by your parents or guardians.

You have the right to say no to adults who use their adult authority to force or coerce you into sexual acts.

You have the right to stand up for yourself and you have the right to get help for yourself when you need it.

I will try to be there when you need me, dear Elizabeth, but, more importantly, I will try to give you the knowledge and convictions and confidence to help you be a survivor in this world even when I am not there.

Of course, Elizabeth, my daughter, doesn't exist yet.

But you do.

Whoever you are.

I decided today to let Susan read all my diaries, including the first one. She'll be the first person to read it. She told me it might help some of her other clients to read my story. I told her that would be okay.

So I am still talking to a "you" I don't know. But I can imagine you--the way I imagined my daughter to be.

Perhaps you are someone like me in some ways. Perhaps you dream, worry, plan, hope, lose hope, get embarrassed, get scared, get mad, think you're crazy, think you're great, watch people, and eat doughnuts. Perhaps you like the Autumn and Spring as I do, and think about being famous, or being grown-up, or running away with someone. Perhaps you have good things in your life. And problems.

Perhaps you have problems like mine.

If you do, please talk, please get help. Learn to like yourself, learn to trust yourself, learn to be yourself.

Learn to be a survivor.

Like me.

AFTERWORD

DEAR ELIZABETH is a fictional account of one young person's efforts to deal with sexual abuse. In real life there are in the United States right now perhaps a million or more young people who are dealing with this problem in their own lives. In 65% to 80% of the cases children are sexually abused by someone they already know--an acquaintance, a friend or a relative. In DEAR ELIZABETH Brenda is molested by her father. This kind of incestuous sexual abuse is usually a very secret crime. Most child victims do not report sexual abuse immediately--in fact, the molestation usually occurs many times over a period of many years, as it did in Brenda's case.

Brenda's story illustrates many typical features of child sexual abuse, but it is one story of one person's abuse. Young people who have been sexually abused may recognize some aspects of Brenda's experience as similar to their own; but they may also find differences between their experiences, feelings and thoughts and those expressed by Brenda in her diary.

Sexual touching by a parent is confusing to children because it creates a mixture of positive and negative feelings. Brenda, for example, talks of enjoying her father hugging her when she was afraid, but she comes to despise his touch after it invades her sexual privacy. This ambivalence--wanting a parent's atten- tion and touch while fearing and disliking that par- ent's sexual abuse--is common among sexually abused children. Some victims may feel the positive aspects of this ambivalence even more strongly than Brenda did and may experience less anger and less guilt than she did.

Almost all children, however, experience the feelings Brenda had after disclosing her sexual abuse. Guilt, depression and fear are prevalent emotions during this period. Brenda talks of wanting to die. She is fearful of what will happen to her father, her mother, her home. She suffers from her brother's rejection and anger. She feels responsible for the break-up of the family. All of these reactions are common among abuse victims; but many also feel a stronger anger toward the perpetrator than Brenda seems to feel toward her father.

Another prevalent concern of child victims is the fear of physical and emotional damage resulting from the abuse. Brenda is relieved after her medical examina- tion to learn she has no physical damage and that it will be possible for her to have satisfactory sexual relationships in the future.

The course of Brenda's therapy with Susan Fogelman represents a frequent pattern among young victims. Therapy is very often helpful at first, but after a short time many victims--especially adolescents--stop attending. Unfortunately, the trauma of sexual abuse may require more extended therapy--as Brenda discovered when an unpleasant experience with her friend Scott dredged up a host of unresolved issues and feelings. Brenda realizes she has only dealt with some of the initial problems and that she needs more help from both individual and group therapy.

In returning to therapy Brenda demonstrates the healing process that is possible for those who have been sexually abused. She grows in confidence, self-esteem and social ability and begins the hopeful process of blossoming into a healthier and happier young woman. And in the course of time she be-comes not a victim but a survivor.

Such an ending--or rather, such a beginning--is surely possible for many other survivors.

ABOUT THE AUTHORS

HELEN SWAN, M.S.W.

Helen Swan has served as an adjunct faculty member for the Menninger Foundation, Kansas and Nebraska State Law Enforcement Academies, Washington University in St. Louis and the Villages Group Homes, Inc. She has been employed as a state training consultant by the states of Kansas, Mississippi, Missouri, Oklahoma and Nebraska.

She has conducted presentations on investigating, treating and preventing sexual child abuse throughout the United States as well as at international conferences in Canada, France and Holland. She has clinically evaluated and treated hundreds of children and offenders since 1977 and has testified as an expert witness in such cases in four different states.

Ms. Swan is the 1986 recipient of the Donna Stone Award, presented by the National Committee for Prevention of Child Abuse for outstanding contributions in the prevention of child abuse.

GENE MACKEY, M.A.

Gene Mackey founded the Waldo Astoria Children's Theatre in 1974, which became THEATRE FOR YOUNG AMERICA in 1977. Gene serves as Artistic Director for TYA, having directed over 125 productions for young audiences.

With an M.A. for the University of Illinois, Gene also studied at New York University, the American Academy of Dramatic Arts, and the University of Arkansas. Gene served as Artistic Director of Casa Manana Playhouse in Ft. Worth, Texas for 4 years.

Also a prolific writer, Gene has written over 40 plays, including *Bubbylonian Encounter*, which deals with good and bad touching and is currently being produced in over 20 states, as well as *Dear Elizabeth*, a diary for incest survivors.

Anatomically Correct Dolls

ANATOMICALLY CORRECT DOLLS

KIDSRIGHTS® own anatomically correct dolls are the finest dolls available, with an unconditional guarantee!

Dealing with suspected young abuse victims is oftentimes difficult; they may be reticent to communicate and perhaps unaware of the correct terminology necessary to communicate.

Dolls aid the child and the interviewer. Non-English speaking children, very young children, and the handicapped are less inhibited when using dolls to describe an incident.

Professionals use this invaluable aid to help their young victims recount events and vent their frustrations in therapy.

KIDSRIGHTS dolls are not toys. Currently in use nationwide in the offices of police, courts, investigators, therapists, and interviewers. Each doll is completely anatomically correct, including an open mouth and tongue, and separate bendable fingers. Extremely durable; able to withstand heavy use. KIDSRIGHTS dolls come fully clothed--including underwear.

KIDSRIGHTS OWN

IN USE NATIONWIDE

ADULTS ARE 18" TALL

CHILDREN ARE 14" TALL

100% FULLY WASHABLE

COMPLETELY ANATOMICALLY CORRECT

FULLY CLOTHED INCLUDING UNDERGARMENTS

DURABLE CONSTRUCTION

UNCONDITIONALLY GUARANTEED

LIGHT, HISPANIC, AND DARK SKIN TONES

IN STOCK FOR IMMEDIATE DELIVERY

#4457 Four Doll Family $259.00
One each of adult & child, male & female.

#4458 Six Doll Family $389.00
One each of adult, grandparent, & child, male & female.

Any doll may be ordered individually at:
                                $69.95 each

#4451 Female Child   #4454 Male Adult
#4452 Male Child   #4455 Grandmother
#4453 Female Adult   #4456 Grandfather

Please specify skin tone when ordering - Light, Hispanic, or Dark.

KIDSRIGHTS CARRYING BAG FOR KIDSRIGHTS DOLLS

A convenient way to transport your anatomically correct dolls. Tough, roomy, durable nylon, with handles. Plenty of room for a complete six doll family and related supplies. Assorted colors imprinted with KIDSRIGHTS logo.

#4486 Carrying Bag $19.95

LIFE LIKE BABY

This adorable, 17" long baby doll is made of soft vinyl and is fully washable and poseable, with jointed arms, legs, and head. Its realistic body has been meticulously detailed. Anatomically correct for complete realism. Baby wears a disposable diaper and a hospital I.D. wristband. Birthing, high school parenting, and sex education classes will find this the next best thing to a real baby.

#4459 Asian Boy   #4462 Black Girl
#4460 Asian Girl   #4463 White Boy
#4461 Black Boy   #4464 White Girl

                        $49.95 each
    2+ $44.95 each   4+ $39.95 each

MINI LIFELIKE BABY

Our smallest babies are only 6½ inches long and are made of soft, powder-scented vinyl. Their anatomically correct bodies show every detail and include perfectly sculpted little hands and feet. Can be used to augment a hospital playroom, or play therapy unit, as well as regular and pre-school classrooms.

#5416 White Girl $9.95
#5417 White Boy $9.95